Look Out!

Poems for children

Chosen by
Neil Nuttall
and
Andy Hawkins

Illustrated by Kay Widdowson

PONT

First Impression—1999

ISBN 1 85902 792 X

© text: the poets
© illustrations: Kay Widdowson

Cover Design: Olwen Fowler

This book is published with the support
of an 'Arts for All' National Lottery
grant from the Arts Council of Wales.

CRONFA LOTERI
LOTTERY FUND

Printed in Wales at Gomer Press, Llandysul, Ceredigion SA44 4QL.

Contents

Learning

I'd like to learn to do my sums
So I could smile when teacher comes
And say I've learned to count and add
And multiply – that can't be bad?
I'd like to learn to take away
And then divide – that's hard they say.
Perhaps I'll learn to tell the time.
I'll measure things and draw a line.

First day at school. That's all I need –
This afternoon I'll learn to read.

Phil Carradice

Ben Alone

Everyone says
I'm a big boy now,
Such a big boy now
that I've started school.
I'm having a busy day.
It's cool.
But my best friend Donut
will bark and moan
And wonder why
We're both alone.

Nicola Davies

Who?

Who looks like a monkey
caged up in the zoo?
You do.

Who makes me wash behind my ears
and stops me having fun?
You've got it. My mum.

Who's that goodie-two-shoes
I would like to smother?
Correct! My brother.

Who's got a face that's round and red
And ugly as a blister?
Who else? My sister.

Whose father's sent him off to bed,
alone, without his tea?
Can you believe it?

Me!

Phil Carradice

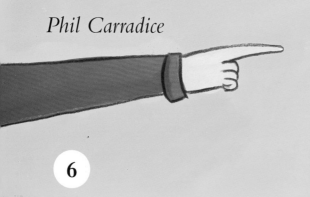

What the Baby Says

You might think
I'm screaming;
You might think
I'm crying.
I just can't manage
Real words,
But I'm trying,
Oh I'm trying!
I really, really
Want to speak.
Perhaps I'll learn how
By next week!

Francesa Kay

Counting Your Chickens

1 is a finger which looks like a skittle.
When I was just one I spoke very little.

2? That's the number of arms that I've got.
3's for the piggies – the wolf ate the lot.

Now 4, that's the legs on a donkey or horse,
The same as on cats and dogs – well, of course.

And 5? That's the age I started this school.
I must learn to count. I feel such a fool.

6, that's the time when we sit down to tea –
Our dog and our cat, dad, mother and me.

7 is simply the days of the week
While 8 is the time the sun starts to peek

In through my curtains – the day will be fine.
Then off into school, I get there by 9.

And 10, that's the number of fingers and toes
On the ends of my arms and feet in neat rows.

Phil Carradice

If Bees Make Honey

If bees make honey
    In a busy hive,
Do ants make marmalade
    From nine 'til five?

Do ladybirds make jam
    In the flower-bed?
Do spiders make syrup
    In the garden shed?

Do beetles make chutney
    In the compost heap?
Do moths make mustard
    When we're fast asleep?

If bees sold the honey
    They made in their hive,
Would they pack their combs
    And head for St. Ives?

Huw Jones

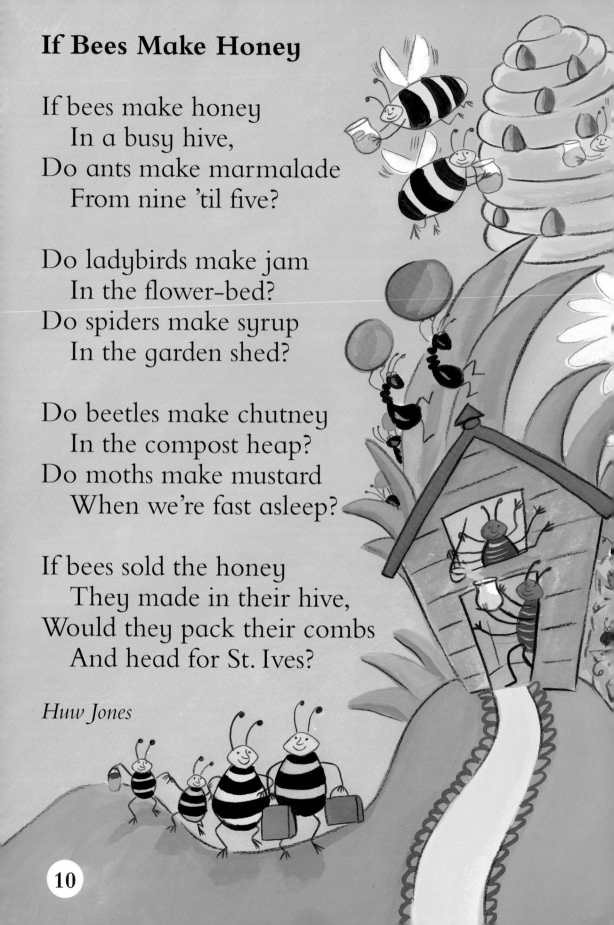

Peaceful Summer Days

There are ants and bees and little trees
And flowers by the dozen,
And scents and smells to make you sneeze –
All over your young cousin!

He's only small, he doesn't know
The way to carry on.
A caterpillar down his back –
There's peaceful, now he's gone.

Phil Carradice

Whatever the Weather

Ice-cream weather, chocolate flake,
　　Candyfloss and pop;
Mince-pie weather, sizzling bangers,
　　Bowls of Dracula soup.

Picnic-weather, water-slides,
　　Bikes and climbing frames;
Jigsaw weather, dressing-up,
　　Cartoons and video games.

T-shirt weather, cool new trainers,
　　Shades and baseball caps;
Welly weather, striped umbrellas,
　　Scarves and bobble-hats.

Bunny weather, wobbly lambs,
　　Bogs of burping frogs;
Penguin weather, flying reindeer,
　　Soggy cats and dogs.

There's *such* a lot of weather;
It's bound to last for ever!

Huw Jones

Summer Holidays

Clickety clack,
Clickety clack,
The train is rushing
Down the track.

Clackety click,
Clackety click,
My little brother's
Feeling sick!

Clickety clack,
Clickety clack,
Are you hungry?
Time for a snack!

Clackety click,
Clackety click,
Look at the fields and
The cows. Look! Quick!

Clickety clack,
Clickety clack,
We're off on our holiday,
And we're never coming back!

Francesca Kay

The Snowman

We built the snowman quickly
When we had had our tea.
I said I thought he looked like Bill,
Bill said he looked like me.

He had a carrot for his nose,
So long and straight and red,
With lumps of coal for buttons,
And Gran's hat on his head.

She searched for simply hours –
Gran couldn't find her hat.
The snowman didn't say a word;
He's rather good like that.

All week he stood just watching
While we played in the snow,
Until the sun began to shine
And then he had to go.

He lost his legs on Sunday;
Next day we went to school
So sad that poor old snowman
Had turned into a pool

Of dirty, muddy water.
And lying in it, flat,
All that remained of snowman
Was Granny's bright red hat.

Phil Carradice

Get Away

Zoom away to Zanzibar
   Drive a racing car:

Breakfast in the south of France
   Dinner in Japan
Tea and cake in Argentina
   Supper in Sudan.

Step on board a motor-boat
   Cruise along the coast:

Leaping with the dolphins
   Sliding with the seals
Drifting with the jelly-fish
   A walrus at the wheel.

Dream beneath the duvet
   Tour the Milky Way:

Kick off on Jupiter
   Pass the ball on Mars
Score a try on Saturn
   Bring home a cup of stars.

Huw Jones

St David's Day

Mirror, mirror, on the wall,
Why are you so high and tall?
Here I am with hat and shawl
Standing tiptoe in the hall.
Please look down from your high place
So that I can see my face.

Nicola Davies

Teifion's Leek

Searching here and searching there
We are searching everywhere.
Someone's taken Teifion's leek
That his Auntie grew last week.
Searching here and searching there
Teifion says, 'It's just not fair!'
We are playing hide and seek.
Who has hidden Teifion's leek?
Leeks are green, but Dai is red,
'Very sorry, Miss,' he said.
'You'll not find that leek – you see,
Teifion's leek is inside me.'

Nicola Davies

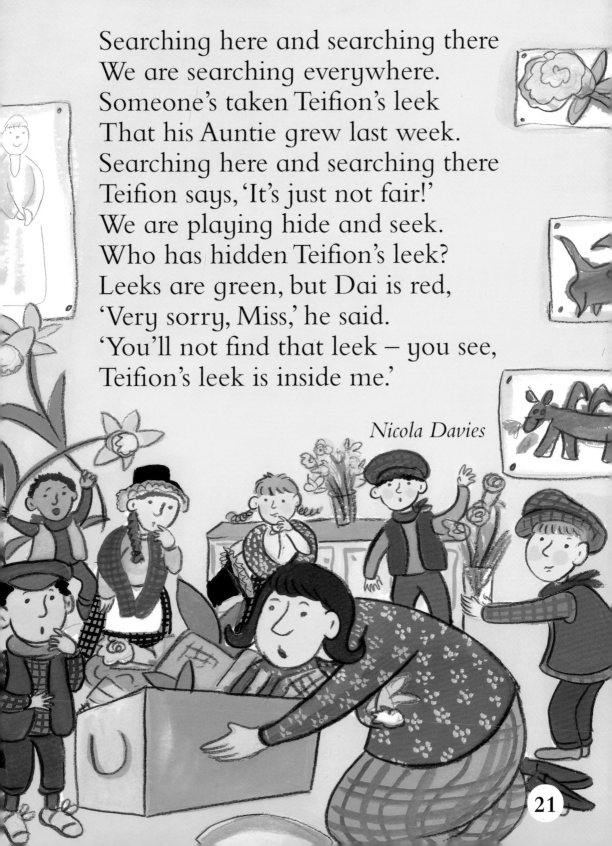

If I Went to Africa

I'd write a trumpet fanfare
For elephants to play;
I'd write a book of jokes
For hyenas to laugh all day.

I'd sell new pin-stripe suits
For zebras to look well-dressed;
I'd sell new spotty jumpers
For leopards to look their best.

I'd teach a pair of giraffes
To waltz between the trees;
I'd teach a class of snakes
To recite their ABC.

I'd open a sauna for hippos
To wash away the mud;
I'd open a beauty salon
So wart hogs feel they're loved.

I'd start a taxi-service
For monkeys to travel in style;
But I'd never, ever start
A crèche for crocodiles.

Huw Jones

Going Nuts

Waking after winter sleep
To skip, to leap, to scamper,
Fribble about in sunbeams
Raid my picnic hamper.

Tag in the leaves, hide and seek,
Climb my favourite tree,
Chase the birds then chase my tail
'Til I'm getting dizzy.

But now I'm feeling bored
Playing on a woodland stage,
So if you could excuse me
I'm off to another page.

Huw Jones

Dream

The other night I went for a ride
On a beautiful snow-white horse.
It flew in the air through the night-time sky
(With me on its back, of course).

Beside the horse flew a mermaid
Her scales reflecting the stars
And as well as a rainbow there glowed
                              in the dark
Venus and Neptune and Mars.

Jenny Sullivan

Ben and Me at Mumbles

We like the sand, we like the sea,
We like each other, Ben and me.

We like to run, we like to play,
We like to fly Ben's kite all day.

Birds wave their wings, fish flick their fins
And where I finish, Ben begins.

I have the collar, Ben the hair,
I bark, he laughs, we fill the air.

We love the pier, the sand, the sea,
We love each other, Ben and me.

Nicola Davies

Thank You, Bones

I wave my arms when I make a fuss,
I flap my hands to stop the bus.
Thank you, bones.

I curve my fingers on the piano keys,
I grasp my fork to eat my peas.
Thank you, bones.

My knees bend as I kneel down,
They creak a bit as I run around.
Thank you, bones.

I shake my head to say, OH NO,
I wiggle my toes and I'm set to GO!
Thank you, bones.

I nod my head to say, OH YES,
I shrug my shoulders, 'It's not my mess.'
Thank you, bones.

My joints and bones are really BRILL,
For I can move about at WILL!
Thank you, bones!

Francesca Kay

School's Out!

School's out
Scream and shout
Kick the ball around.
Hometime
Roamtime
Jump and shout and bound.
Sun's bright
Night's light
Playing in the park.
Sadtime
Bedtime
Just as it grows dark.

Jenny Sullivan

It's My Bedroom

My Mam is all purple and shouting
She's saying my room is a sty;
She's stamping and tearing her hair out
I really don't understand why.

My sweater's OK on the lampshade
My trainers are fine on the floor;
My nightie is draped on the wardrobe
And my coat's on the knob of the door.

Mam says that my gerbils are choking
From my smelly old socks on the cage
And my library book is all greasy
From the chip sandwich marking my page.

I can't see a problem with wellies
Each side by side on the chair;
They're great for chucking old crisp bags
And next time it rains—they are there!

I tell her, 'You need to calm down, Mam!
Don't get your old self in a tizz.
My bedroom may be a *bit* messy
But *I* know where everything is!'

Night Sounds

When I close my eyes in bed at night
   Do you know what I can hear?
The old house creak, the wild owls hoot
   And the sounds of my family, near.

Brothers and sisters all over the house
   Doing brotherly, sisterly things,
And Mum downstairs in the kitchen
   (When my Mum is happy, she sings).

My brother is playing his Gameboy –
   I can hear it squiggle and bleep;
I listen a while then I sit up and shout,
   'Turn it off, 'cos I can't go to sleep!'

The telly is on in my Mamgu's room,
   My Dad's mending stuff in his shed,
All of my family, night time sounds
   And me, snug and safe in my bed.

Jenny Sullivan